RACE
AGAINST BULLYING

The Dollar General Literacy Foundation was established in 1993 in honor of Dollar General's co-founder, J.L. Turner, who was functionally illiterate with only a third grade education. He was a farmer's son who dropped out of school when his father was killed in an accident. With determination and hard work, he began what has now become a successful company.

We understand sometimes life circumstances prevent individuals from learning to read or graduating from high school, but it's never too late to learn. Through funding initiatives, we are committed to helping individuals of all ages learn to read, prepare for their high school equivalency or learn English.

To learn more about the Dollar General Literacy Foundation, please visit www.dgliteracy.org.

DOLLAR GENERAL®
Save time. Save money. **Every day!**®

Bendon
Ashland, OH 44885
www.bendonpub.com

Series created by: Matt and Katie Kenseth
Written by: Gina Gold
Illustrated by: Adam Devaney
Produced by: Judy O Productions, Inc.

ISBN: 1-63109-516-1

Visit us at www.bendonpub.com

Long before I became a NASCAR champion or even before I knew what I wanted to be when I grew up, I was just a boy raised by a Christian family in Cambridge, Wisconsin.

As a kid, I experienced many of the same struggles our children face today. Now, as a father of four, I want to help my kids have a better understanding of some of these issues and equip them with the tools they will need to do the right thing when the opportunity presents itself.

Hopefully, this book will help you and your children openly discuss the challenges that come with bullying and ways they can handle this issue.

Good luck,

Matt Kenseth

It was Matt's first day of fourth grade. He couldn't wait to tell his friend Katie about his summer racing mini stock cars. Matt loved to race — turning wrenches, going fast, and seeing that checkered flag wave. He was going to be a racing champion.

However, a new kid decided to take Matt down a notch.

"You think you're a big shot in your racing shirt, but I bet I can run faster than you can drive," he boasted, then laughed with his friend.

"He's that new boy, Eddie," Katie said. "Just ignore him."

The teasing didn't stop.

"You sure walk slow," Eddie called out, as he splashed water onto Matt's shirt. "I hope you're faster than that on the track."

Matt asked Katie why a boy he didn't even know would be mean to him.

"He's just jealous because you're a great racer," Katie said.

Matt decided to put the bad morning behind him.
He was having a great time tossing a football around
with his friend Joe. Just then, Eddie stepped in and
caught Matt's pass.

"See, that's what it means to be fast, race geek," Eddie said, throwing the ball hard at Matt. Eddie ran off laughing.

After school, Matt's mom asked how the day went. "Do you like your teacher?"

"Mr. Kramer's very nice," Matt said, "but there's this kid... Oh, never mind..."

"Do you think racing's silly?" Matt asked his dad,
as he handed him a wrench.

"Silly? Nothing's silly if you love to do it. You do
love racing, right, Matt?"

"More than anything," Matt agreed.

Later, Matt wondered if the new boy might be right.

He asked Katie and Joe, "Do you think I'm weird because I love to race?"

"No way," said Joe. "I think it's the coolest thing ever."

"That's right," Katie added. "We know you're great. Don't let that new kid tell you otherwise."

The next morning, Matt didn't feel like going to school.

"What's wrong?" his mother asked. "Are you sick?"

"No…" Matt said. He couldn't lie, but didn't want to talk about the mean kid at school.

"You can always tell us what's bothering you," his father said.

"Well," said Matt taking a deep breath. "There's this new kid at school who was being mean to me and making fun of my racing yesterday."

Matt's dad said they were glad Matt spoke up, "It's never good to keep bullying to yourself."

On the way to school, Matt's dad explained that life has many challenges. He added Matt can always be proud of who he is and what he loves to do – no matter what anyone says.

"That's right," his mother chimed in. "No one can take that away. If someone doesn't like who you are, they just don't know you well enough."

Matt and his parents brainstormed solutions to the problem. Together they came up with a 3-step plan.

1) If Eddie bothered Matt again, Matt should ignore him.

2) If Eddie kept teasing him, Matt should tell him firmly, but politely, to stop.

3) If it happened yet again, Matt should stay calm, walk away, and tell a teacher.

Matt felt much better now that he knew what to do.

The day was going perfectly, until...

"Hey, racer boy. Vroom, Vroom," Eddie called out.

"I'm ignoring him," Matt told Katie and Joe, remembering Step I. "Let's play somewhere else."

But, Eddie followed them. "What's the matter, racer boy? Are you..."

Before Eddie could finish, Matt jumped in —

"My name's not 'racer boy' it's Matt. And yes, I love to race. So please leave me alone," Matt said, relying on Step 2.

"Oh, yeah?" Eddie said, and shoved Matt.

Matt wanted to push Eddie back, but instead, he remembered Step 3. He went to talk to his teacher, Mr. Kramer.

Mr. Kramer sent the boys and their families to meet with Suzie, the school counselor.

Matt told the counselor that Eddie had made fun of him for racing.

Eddie said he didn't mean anything by it. He was just playing around. After Susie asked more questions, Eddie admitted he was scared going to a new school and had teased Matt to look important.

The next day, Eddie apologized to Matt.

"I'm sorry I teased you," he said. "I actually think you're pretty cool."

"Apology accepted," Matt said, and he invited Eddie to his next race.

Matt felt great he had handled a difficult situation well. Now, no matter what anyone said about him, he would always be proud that he loved racing.

"Thank you for your help and support," he called out to his friends and family. "And remember, if you believe in yourself, you're always a winner!"

Bullying can happen anywhere – not just at school. There are many types of bullying. The statistics are alarming. More than 2.7 million students are bullied each year and one out of every seven students in grades K-12 reports they have been victims of bullying or have bullied another child.

Everyone has a role they can play in preventing bullying. It starts with respect and caring for others. Please take a moment to educate yourself and your family on bullying by visiting websites such as StopBullying.gov or one of the other resources listed below.

Together, we can make a difference.

RESOURCES:

www.StopBullying.gov

www.DoSomething.org

www.StopBullyingNowFoundation.org